The children were in the pool.

Wilma climbed on the duck.

"Get on," said Wilma.

Wilf climbed on.

"Get on," said Wilf.

Chip climbed on.

"Get on," said Chip.

Biff climbed on.

"Get on," said Biff.

Kipper couldn't get on.

"Get on," said everyone.

Kipper couldn't get on.

"Get on," said everyone.

Kipper climbed on.

Oh no!